Fred

RUPERT FAWCETT

ARROW BOOKS

FRED SPENT THE EVENING ADMIRING
HIS CORNFLAKE COLLECTION.

FRED DISTINCTLY REMEMBERED
ASKING PIP <u>NOT</u> TO BRING
HIS NEPHEW.

'THAT'S THE LAST TIME WE BUY
KAT-O-MUNCH', RESOLVED FRED.

'ILL BE ABLE TO GO TO UNCLE CLAUDES PARTY AFTER ALL' ENTHUSED FRED UPON FINDING HIS WINGS.

HAVING SUCCESSFULLY HYPNOTISED ANTHONY FRED TURNED TO CHAPTER EIGHT, 'THE UNCONSCIOUS FELINE.'

FRED STILL OWED
PENELOPE 20ᴾ.

FRED SAT DOWN TO ENJOY
A SPOT OF LUNCH.

'WHATS A STRETCH LIMMO?' ASKED
FRED, READING PENELOPE'S BIRTHDAY
PRESENT SUGGESTION LIST.

FRED'S QUICK REFLEXES SAVED
THE SAUSAGE ROLLS.

'DOWN!' SNAPPED FRED.

SO FAR AS THE CREAM HORNS
WERE CONCERNED, IT WAS GOING
TO BE EVERY MAN FOR HIMSELF.

FRED COULDN'T DECIDE
WHICH NOSE TO WEAR
TO MARTHA'S WEDDING.

AFTER DINNER FRED
SHOWED EVERYONE THE
UNEXPLODED BOMB.

'BUT IM ALWAYS THE REAR END', GRISLED PENELOPE.

FRED'S LOLLIPOP SOON HAD
THE DESIRED EFFECT.

FRED'S POND WAS AN ENDLESS
SOURCE OF PLEASURE TO HIM.

FRED'S OPERATION WAS
A RESOUNDING SUCCESS.

PENELOPE AND FRED PAID
THEIR RESPECTS AT THE SHRINE
OF THE HOLY CUP-CAKE.

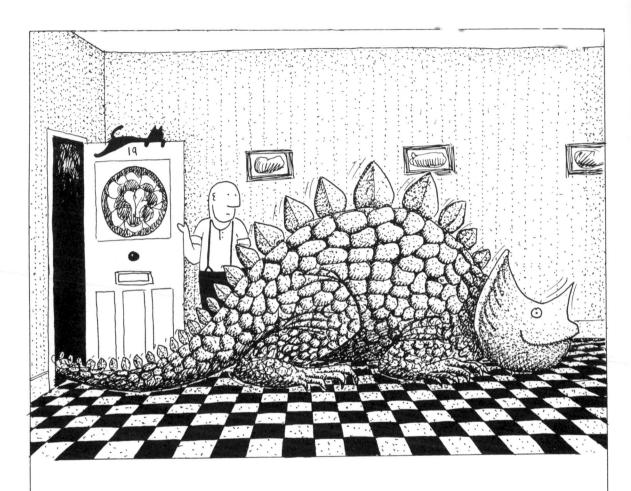

'NO PEACE FOR THE WICKED,'
SIGHED FRED.

FRED FOUND WINNING AT CHESS
IMMENSELY GRATIFYING.

AFTER DINNER FRED
SERENADED PENELOPE
WITH HIS ALPINE HORN.

PIP SEEMED RELUCTANT TO TRY
FRED'S PNEUMATIC TOOTHPICK.

FRED HAD REACHED CHAPTER TWO,
'THE ART OF FOREPLAY'.

FRED TRIED NOT TO
STARE AT OSCAR'S HEAD.

'NOT ANOTHER FULL MOON,'
GROANED PENELOPE.

FRED WAS BECOMING INCREASINGLY
SECURITY—CONSCIOUS.

IT WAS ANTHONY'S FIRST
SESSION WITH THE ANIMAL
PSYCHOTHERAPIST.

FRED AND PENELOPE ALWAYS
DREADED LOOKING AFTER
THE NESBIT'S DOG.

FRED SPENT MANY HOURS
PERFECTING HIS PICKLED
ONION AFTERSHAVE.

PENELOPE AND FRED FINALLY
PERFECTED THEIR HUMAN PYRAMID.

FRED FINALLY CONFESSED TO
EATING THE SOFA.

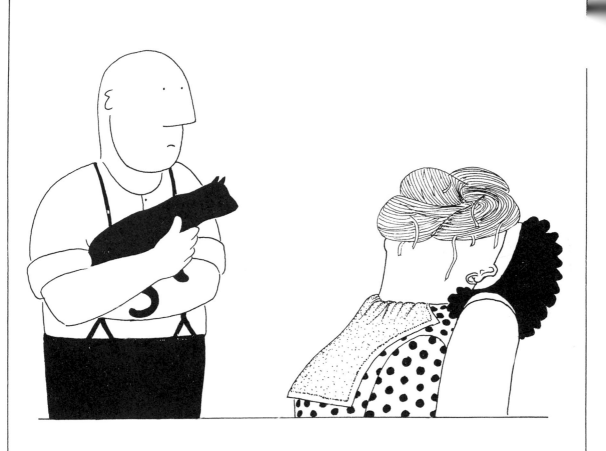

EVERY SUNDAY PENELOPE TREATED HERSELF TO A SPAGHETTI FACE-PACK.

PONCHOS AND TURBANS
WERE IN AGAIN.

EACH DAY STARTED WITH A
VIGOROUS WORK-OUT.

FRED MADE SURE HE NEVER
LOST AT PING-PONG.

EVERYBODY POINTED TO THEIR
FAVOURITE PART OF THE WALL.

PENELOPE'S CHOCOLATE DETECTOR
PROVED EFFECTIVE.

FRED AND PENELOPE PROVIDED
THEIR GUESTS WITH AFTER-
DINNER ENTERTAINMENT.

FRED SENSED THAT ALL WAS
NOT WELL WITH PIP.

THE EVENING WAS SPENT TESTING
PENELOPE'S NEW LABOUR-SAVING
LIPSTICK APPLICATOR.

FRED ASKED MR AND MRS NESBIT
TO LEAVE VIA THE SECRET TUNNEL.

UNDER THE COMPOST HEAP FRED
FOUND A BONE HE BURIED DURING
ONE OF HIS DOG PHASES.

IT LOOKED LIKE IT WAS
GOING TO BE 'ONE OF
THOSE DAYS'.

THE BABY POLTERGEIST WAS BACK.

CONSTANCE AND PIP WERE THE
FIRST TO ARRIVE AT FRED AND
PENELOPE'S TOOTHACHE PARTY.

'SO THIS IS THE SIXTY-NINE
POSITION', SAID FRED GRIMLY.

MR AND MRS NESBIT WERE THE
FIRST TO ARRIVE AT FRED AND
PENELOPE'S ZEBRA-CROSSING PARTY.

FRED REALISED PENELOPE HADN'T
BEEN EXAGGERATING ABOUT HER
COUSIN FRANK AFTER ALL.

FRED WROTE THE
SHOPPING LIST WITH
HIS NEW WATERPROOF PEN.

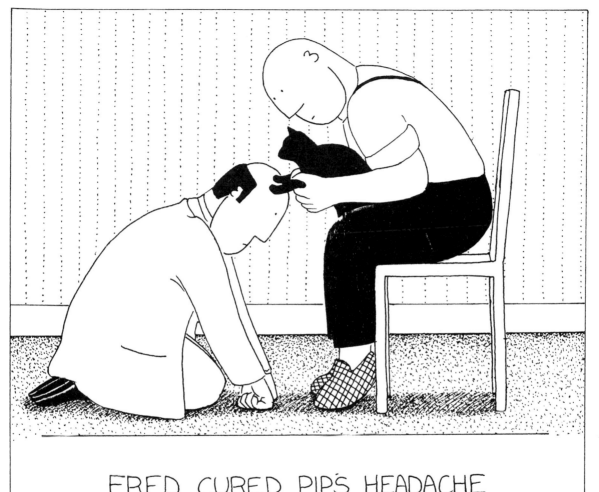

FRED CURED PIP'S HEADACHE
WITH A LAYING-ON-OF-PAWS.

FRED'S URGE TO BUILD A
SNOWMAN WAS FRUSTRATED
BY A LACK OF SNOW.

FRED ASKED CONSTANCE
AND PIP NOT TO WALK
ON THE NEW CARPET.

FRED NEVER FORGOT THE
TRICKS HIS FATHER TAUGHT
HIM AS A BOY.

FRED MADE A MENTAL NOTE NOT TO
FORGET PENELOPE'S BIRTHDAY AGAIN.

PENELOPE SENT FRED UPSTAIRS
FOR THE BIG TEAPOT.

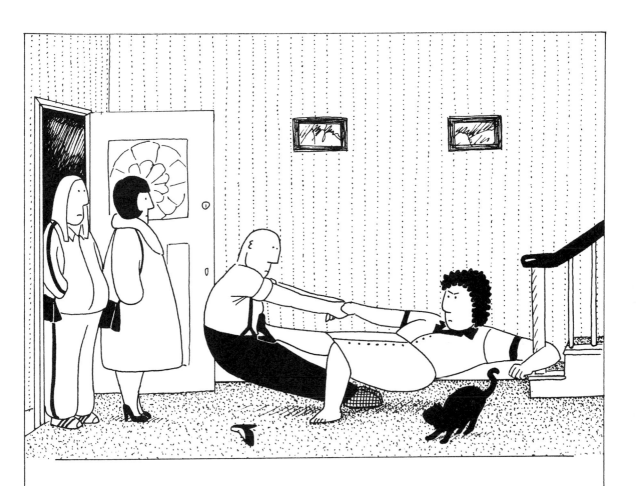

PENELOPE APPEARED TO BE
LOSING INTEREST IN HER
WEIGHT-WATCHERS MEETINGS.

'HAVE YOU BEEN RUBBING THAT LAMP AGAIN?' GROWLED PENELOPE.

FRED WAS IN THE MOOD
FOR LOVE.

FRED 'FLOSSED' HIS GUESTS
BETWEEN EACH COURSE.

'THAT'S THE LAST TIME WE USE PREHISTORIC DECORATORS,' FUMED FRED.

FRED COULD FEEL A
NOVEL COMING ON.